Plate II

Niantic
Late 17th Century
Northeastern Woodland

Mohawk
Early 18th Century
Northeastern Woodland

Plate I

Paiute
Late 19th Century
Great Basin

Souix Warrior
Late 19th Century
Plains

Plate IV

Seminole
Early 19th Century
Southeastern Woodland

Seminole
Modern
Southeastern Woodland

Plate V

Cherokee
Early 19th Century
Southeastern Woodland

Plate VI

Menominee
Early 19th Century
Northeastern Woodland

Chippewa
Early 19th Century
Northeastern Woodland

Plate VII

Mandan
Early 19th Century
Plains

Plate VIII

Kiowa
19th Century
Plains

Dakota (Souix)
19th Century
Plains

Dakota (Souix)
19th Century
Plains

Plate IX

Cheyenne-Arapaho
White Woman Buffalo Ceremonial
Plains

Arapaho
Late 19th Century
Ghost Dance Ceremonial
Plains

Plate X

Blackfoot
19th Century
Plains

Blackfoot
Medicine Man
19th Century
Plains

Plate XI

Hupa
19th Century
California

Tlingit
Traditional Ceremonial
Northwest Coast

Plate XII

Nez Percé
Late 19th Century
Plateau

Plate XIII

Hopi
Traditional
Southwest

Yavapai
Late 19th Century
Southwest

Plate XIV

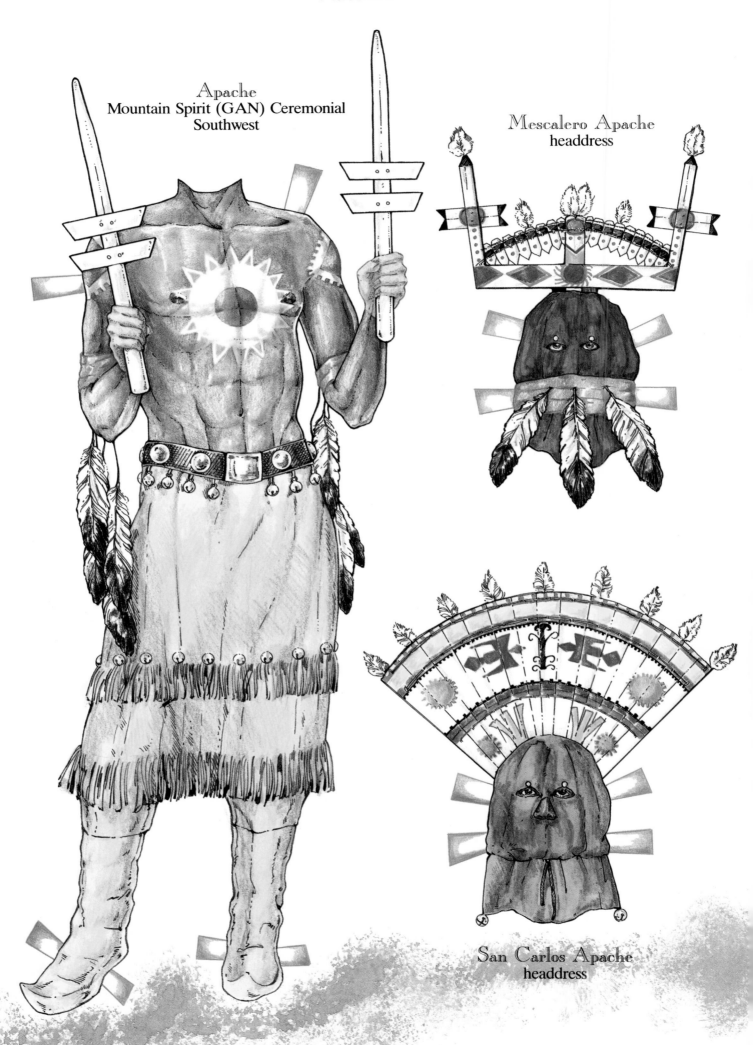

Apache
Mountain Spirit (GAN) Ceremonial
Southwest

Mescalero Apache
headdress

San Carlos Apache
headdress

Plate XV

Pueblo
ue Corn Maiden Ceremonial
Southwest

Yaqui
Deer Dancer
Southwest